Welcome to the Journey!

Oh, the depth of the riches both of the wisdom

and knowledge of God! How unsearchable are

His judgments and unfathomable His ways!

For who has known the mind of the Lord,

or who became His counselor?"...For from

Him and through Him and to Him are

all things. To Him be the glory forever! Amen.

— Romans 11:33-34, 36

GOD: AS HE LONGS FOR YOU TO SEE HIM STUDY GUIDE

GOD

AS HE LONGS FOR YOU TO SEE HIM

INTRODUCTION ～

> *"I know nothing which can so comfort the soul; so calm the swelling billows of sorrow and grief; so speak peace to the winds of trial, as a devout musing upon the subject of the Godhead."*
>
> – C. S. Lewis

About this Study

We're glad you decided to study the character of God. This could be one of the most important studies you have ever done. What's unique about this study is that it come in three parts. It's best to use all of these components because they all complement each other. You may find if you just use the DVD and the Small Group study that you miss out on some important teaching from the book. We encourage you to use all three.

- ～ BOOK: God, As He Longs for You to See Him by Chip Ingram
- ～ DVD: Chip Ingram teaches a 15 minute lesson on each attribute of God
- ～ STUDY GUIDE/JOURNAL: Your guide to think and pray through your experience in this study. The study guide follows the DVD, not the book

---

During the week:
- ～ *Read the chapter assigned for that week*
- ～ *Complete the corresponding journal section*

During the group time:
- ～ *Watch the video*
- ～ *Work through video questions/fill-ins*
- ～ *Be ready to discuss*

"Our aim in studying the Godhead must be to know God Himself better. Our concern must be to enlarge our acquaintance, not simply with the doctrine of God's attributes, but with the living God whose attributes they are."
— J. I. Packer

WATCH VIDEO

1. When you think of God's existence, how do you perceive the culture is thinking about Him? What do you think other people are thinking about when they ponder God?

_____

_____

2. If you were forced to describe God with one word, what word would you use and why?

_____

_____

3. Share with the group one thing you are hoping to get out of this study.

_____

_____

 From Head to Heart

Think of someone in your circle (maybe at the office, in the neighborhood, or at your school) and let them know you are studying the existence of God. With no pressure, ask them the first two questions above. Report the responses to the group. You may find the answers surprising.

Assignment for Next Week

Read Chapters 1–3
Use the journal of this study guide to carry your through the reading assignment.

REMINDER

1. Confidentiality – *What is said in the group stays in the group. Let's assure each other that everyone is safe to share.*

2. No pressure – *Everyone has the option to pass. In fact it's best not to go in a circle every time to answer questions. Share "popcorn style." Allow people to speak as they are led.*

3. Care for one another – *This is not a teaching session as much as it is an opportunity to love and care for others. Pray for each other during the week. Find ways to check in on people in your group.*

GOD

AS HE LONGS FOR YOU TO SEE HIM

God: As He Longs for You to See Him

2

SESSION TWO

Seeing God with 20/20 Vision

Grandfather in a rocking chair.

Cosmic cop.

Blind watchmaker.

What's your picture of God? Does He smile down at us with a wink and a nod? Does He wait to pounce when we break his laws? Did He wind up the universe and move on to the next galaxy? Even if it's an empty frame, we all have our own portrait of this entity known more commonly as God.

A. W. Tozer, an American pastor and writer during the 20th century, wrote, "What comes into our minds when we think about God is the most important thing about us." How we see God will determine in large part how we view ourselves. Are we loved? Are we under scrutiny? Does anyone really care?

There are two crucial questions we must answer: what is our perception of God and is it right? Like viewing God through distorted lenses, many of us make three common mistakes when we imagine what God looks like:

- We tend to assume that God is just like us.
- We tend to reduce Him to measurable and controllable terms.
- We tend to overlook the obvious and significant ways that He has revealed Himself to us.

Nothing in all your life will impact your relationship with God, your relationship with people, your self-view, your decisions, and your purpose like the way you think of God. This week we start with a profound truth: He wants you to see Him clearly.

Day 1 ∼

Read chapters 1-2 in *God: As He Longs for You to See Him*.
What have been some of your misperceptions of
God? How has that affected the way you live?

_____

_____

_____

_____

_____

_____

_____

_____

_____

_____

_____

_____

_____

_____

_____

_____

_____

_____

_____

_____

_____

_____

_____

_____

*"What you think about
God shapes your whole
relationship with Him.
In addition, what you
believe God thinks
about you determines
how close you will grow
toward Him."*

— Chip

Day 2 ~

What do you think God thinks about you? How do these perceptions affect your relationship with Him?

But whatever things were gain to me, those things I have counted as loss for the sake of Christ. More than that, I count all things to be loss in view of the surpassing value of knowing Christ Jesus my Lord, for whom I have suffered the loss of all things, and count them but rubbish so that I may gain Christ, and may be found in Him, not having a righteousness of my own derived from the law, but that which is through faith in Christ, the righteousness which comes from God on the basis of faith, that I may know Him and the power of His resurrection and the fellowship of His sufferings, being conformed to His death ...

— Philippians 3: 7-10

Day 3 ~
RENEW YOUR MIND

Our vision of who God is can be improved by a clear picture from His Word. Take a moment today to memorize and meditate on this verse:

> The Lord your God is in your midst,
> a victorious warrior
>   He will exult over you with joy,
>   He will be quiet in His love,
>   He will rejoice over you with shouts of joy.
>
>   — Zephaniah 3:17

"As much as it is humanly possible, we must get an accurate, clear picture of who the Creator of the universe is and exactly what He is like...And here's the motivation: until you know God as He is, you'll never become all that He's created you to be."

— Chip

Day 4 ～

Read chapter 3 in *God: As He Longs for You to See Him*. Did you take a moment to stop for a few minutes and think about who God is and what He is like? Reflect on the character of God and your desire to know Him. Give your heart, soul, and mind an opportunity to consider who made you, who loves you, and who longs to be seen clearly by you. At the end, spend a few minutes in prayer with Him. Ask Him to reveal Himself to you.

"We tend by a secret law of the soul to move toward our mental image of God."

— A. W. Tozer

Day 5 ∼

God has revealed Himself in many different ways throughout Scripture. Look at each one of the verses below and describe how God specifically manifested Himself to us.

Psalm 19

_____

_____

_____

John 1:1-4; 14

_____

_____

_____

John 1:17-18; Hebrews 1:3

_____

_____

_____

Read chapter 1
in A. W. Tozer's *Knowledge of the Holy.*

Tools for
Life Change:

*There are two books we recommend that will give additional insight as you continue your journey on the attributes of God. Please consider adding, A. W. Tozer's **Knowledge of the Holy** and J. I. Packer's **Knowing God** to your library.*

Is Your God too Small?

Where were you when I laid the foundation of the earth?
Tell Me, if you have understanding...   — Job 38:4

"How may we form a right idea of God's greatness? First *is to remove from our thoughts of God limits that would make Him small.* The second *is to compare Him with powers and forces which we regard as great.*"

— J. I. Packer

 WATCH VIDEO

In Chapter 1 we learned: What you think about God shapes your relationship with Him.
> ∿ It determines how you perceive God
> ∿ It determines how you think God perceives you
> ∿ It determines how you relate with God
> Isaiah 40:25–28

In Chapter 2 we learned: "We tend by a secret law of the soul to move toward our mental image of God."
> ∿ We tend to assume God is just like us
> ∿ We tend to reduce Him to manageable terms
> ∿ We tend to overlook the obvious and significant
>   ways He has revealed Himself to us

1. _____ Psalm 19
2. _____ John 1:4
3. _____ John 1:17

In Chapter 3 we raised the question: How do I know if I am seeing God as He really is?
> ∿ Take the vision test on page 242 of the book (see page 16 in
> study guide) and rate yourself in the following areas:
>> ∿ Those who know God have great energy for God
>> ∿ Those who know God have great thoughts of God
>> ∿ Those who know God show great boldness for God
>> ∿ Those who know God have great contentment in God

"What comes into our minds when we think about God is the most important thing about us. For this reason the gravest question before the Church is always God himself, and the most portentous fact about any man is not what he at a given time may say or do, but what he in his deep heart conceives God to be like."

— A. W. Tozer

FOUR INDICATORS OF
"SEEING GOD AS HE LONGS TO BE SEEN"

Self Evaluation

1. Those who know God have <u>great energy</u> for God.

2. Those who know God have <u>great thoughts</u> of God.

3. Those who know God show <u>great boldness</u> for God.

4. Those who know God have <u>great contentment</u> in God.

Small Group Questions

1. If you haven't done so, take the vision test on p. 242 of the book or on the previous page in your study guide.

_____

_____

2. Who do you know that has great *energy, thoughts, boldness,* and/or *contentment* for God and give an example?

_____

_____

3. Share specific ways you are personally getting to know God. Is it through His word? His nature?

_____

_____

 From Head to Heart

Who did you put down as someone who has great energy, thoughts, boldness, and/or contentment for God? Set up a lunch or write them a letter and ask this question, "What are your best practices and spiritual disciplines for getting to know God?"

Next Week's Assignment

1. Read Chapter 4 in God: As He Longs for You to See Him or chapter 16 in The Knowledge of the Holy.
2. Consider either Tozer's *Knowledge of the Holy* or J.I. Packer's *Knowing God,* and begin reading with chapter one.
3. Meditate for three minutes on "who God really is" each time before you pray this week.

FACILITATOR T!PS

You don't have to share the vision test scores unless you feel like your group is already transparent enough to do so. It would make a great discussion starter.

God: As He Longs for You to See Him

3

SESSION THREE

The Goodness of God

There's an old story about a Chinese gentleman who lived on the border of China and Mongolia. In those days, there was constant conflict along the perimeter. The Chinese man had a beautiful horse, a mare, who one day leaped over the fence, raced down the road, crossed the border, and was captured by the Mongolians. His friends came to comfort him.

"That's bad news," they said sadly.

"What makes you think it's bad news?" asked the Chinaman. "Maybe it's good news."

A few days later the mare came bolting into his corral, bringing with it a massive, snow white stallion. His friends crowded around. "That's good news!" they cried.

"What makes you think it's good news?" he asked. "Maybe it is bad news."

Later that week, his son was riding the stallion, trying to break it. He was thrown off and he broke his leg. The friends came. "That's bad news," they cried.

"What makes you think it is bad news?" asked the Chinaman. "Maybe it's good news." The next week, war broke out with Mongolia, and a Chinese general came through town drafting all the young men. He took them all and they were all later killed, except for the young man who couldn't go because his leg was broken.

The Chinaman said to his friends, "You see, the things you thought were bad turned out good; and the things you thought were good turned out bad."

If we base our perception of God's goodness on our *circumstances* rather than His *character*, our view will always be shortsighted. This week, let's discover what it means to trust the Lord to work all things together for our benefit.

Day 1 ~

Read chapter 4 in *God: As He Longs for You to See Him.*
How did this chapter clear up your view of God's
goodness?

_____

_____

_____

_____

_____

_____

_____

_____

_____

_____

_____

_____

_____

_____

_____

_____

_____

_____

_____

_____

_____

_____

_____

_____

_____

Prayer for the Week:

*O Lord God, full of
goodness and mercy, as I
look into the face of Jesus
and ponder the goodness
of the cross, grant that
I might repent of my
unbelief and ingratitude,
rest in Your goodness even
in the midst of trial, and
risk trusting You in every
area of my life like never
before.*

*I praise You that I live
under a friendly sky,
that You are for me, and
that I need never be afraid
of the future because You
are good!*

In Jesus' name,

Amen.

Day 2 ~

Do you ever struggle with believing God is out to get you? Do you ever feel guilty for having "too much" fun or feeling "too blessed" as if God may suddenly yank it all away? How does this conflict with the goodness of God?

Every good thing given and every perfect gift is from above, coming down from the Father of lights, with whom there is no variation or shifting shadow. In the exercise of His will He brought us forth by the word of truth, so that we would be a kind of first fruits among His creatures.

— James 1:17-18

Day 3 ~

RENEW YOUR MIND

Our vision of who God is can be improved by a clear picture from His Word. Take a moment today to memorize and meditate on this verse:

For the Lord God is a sun and shield; the Lord gives grace and glory; no good thing does He withhold from those who walk uprightly.

— Psalm 84:11

"*With the goodness of God to desire our highest welfare, the wisdom of God to plan it, and the power of God to achieve it, what do we lack?*"

— A. W. Tozer

Day 4 ~

On pages 68-69 of the book, under the section "How Are We to Respond to God's Goodness?" Chip mentioned that we must repent of our unbelief and ingratitude. Which one do you need to deal with today?

If you have never started a relationship with Christ, make today the day you make a "U-turn" and repent from going the way of your independence and start going the way of dependence upon Christ. Romans 10:9-10 states:

...that if you confess with your mouth Jesus as Lord, and believe in your heart that God raised Him from the dead, you will be saved; for with the heart a person believes, resulting in righteousness, and with the mouth he confesses, resulting in salvation.

Chances are, if you have been a believer for a while, you've started feeling entitled to God's blessing rather than showing gratitude to God for His goodness. This week prior to your prayer times before the Lord, thank Him for five ways He has shown His goodness to You.

"The proper study of a Christian is the Godhead. The highest science, the loftiest speculation, the mightiest philosophy, which can ever engage the attention of a child of God, is the name, the nature, the person, the work, the doings, and the existence of the great God whom he calls his Father."

– Charles Haddon Spurgeon

Day 5 ~

We must believe that God has holy pleasure in the happiness of His people. Are you resting in the goodness of God, or is your mind replaying all the worries of life? Meditate on Psalm 31:19-20. It's hard to believe that everything He has allowed to come into our lives has come through hands that are kind, cordial, and benevolent. Commit to start habitually thanking Him for your circumstances and gifts.

_____

_____

_____

_____

_____

_____

_____

_____

_____

_____

_____

_____

_____

_____

_____

Read chapter 16
in A. W. Tozer's *Knowledge of the Holy.*

Read chapter 16
in J. I. Packer's *Knowing God.*

"The Goodness of God"
Psalm 84:11

 WATCH VIDEO

Sometimes, "Perception is Everything"

~ What we think <u>people</u> "think of us" determines how we respond to them.
~ How we think about <u>God</u> determines how we respond to God.

I.   The Importance of Our Study

"What comes into our minds when we think about God is the most important thing about us.

The history of mankind will probably show that no people has ever risen above its religion, and man's spiritual history will positively demonstrate that no religion has ever been greater than its idea of God. Worship is pure or base as the worshiper entertains high or low thoughts of God.

For this reason the gravest question before the Church is always God Himself, and the most portentous fact about any man is not what he at a given time may say or do, but what he in his deep heart conceives God to be like. **We tend by a secret law of the soul to move toward our mental image of God.** This is true not only of the individual Christian, but of the company of Christians that composes the Church."

A.W. Tozer, *Knowledge of the Holy*

"The goodness of God is that which disposes Him to be kind, cordial, benevolent, and full of good will toward men. He is tenderhearted and of quick sympathy, and His unfailing attitude toward all moral beings is open, frank, and friendly. By His nature He is inclined of bestow blessedness and He takes holy pleasure in the happiness of His people."

A.W. Tozer, *Knowledge of the Holy*

"Within the cluster of God's moral perfections there is one in particular to which the term 'goodness' points – the quality which God specially singled out from the whole when proclaiming 'all his goodness' to Moses, He spoke of Himself as 'abundant in *goodness* and truth' (Exodus 34:6). This is the quality of *generosity*. Generosity means a disposition to give to others in a way which has no mercenary motive and is not limited by what the recipients deserve, but consistently goes beyond it. Generosity expresses the simple wish that others should have what they need to make them happy. Generosity is, so to speak, the focal point of God's moral perfection; it is the quality which determines how all God's other excellences are to be displayed."

J.I. Packer, *Knowing God*

II. How Does God Reveal His Goodness to Us?

1. Through His Blessing – Psalm 145:7-9

2. Through His Deliverance – Psalm 107

   ~ Redeeming the helpless from their enemies

   ~ Rescuing us from the "shadow of death"

   ~ Healing our diseases

   ~ Protection from the storms that threaten to sink our lives

3. Through His Son, Jesus – Mark 10:18

   ~ Romans 5:8 – Undeserved goodness

   ~ Romans 8:32 – The promise of future goodness

   ~ James 1:17-18 – The source of all goodness

Response to God's Goodness

1. Repent _____

2. Rest _____

3. Risk _____

How Are We to <u>Respond</u> to God's Goodness?

1. _____ of our unbelief and ingratitude.

> Or do you show contempt for the riches of his kindness,
> tolerance and patience, not realizing that God's kindness leads
> you toward repentance?
>
> Romans 2:4 (NIV)

2. _____ in His goodness when encountering adversity.

> [19]How great is Your goodness, which You have stored up for
> those who fear You, which You have wrought for those who take
> refuge in You, before the sons of men! [20]You hide them in the
> secret place of Your presence from the conspiracies of man; You
> keep them secretly in a shelter from the strife of tongues.
>
> Psalm 31:19-20 (NASB)

3. _____ stepping out in faith like never before!

> For the LORD God is a sun and shield; the LORD gives grace
> and glory; no good thing does He withhold from those who walk
> uprightly.
>
> Psalm 84:11 (NASB)

Small Group Questions

1. How has this week's study on God's goodness influenced your view of God?

2. Go around the room and give thanks in one sentence for how God has shown His goodness to you.

3. What risk or step of obedience has God prompted you to take that you have not surrendered? Your future? Relationships? Money?

FACILITATOR T!PS

As a facilitator, you will need to "lead out." Your transparency will set the tone for the group.

Remember, go "popcorn style" in sharing.

Be careful of the rabbit trails! People will be tempted to discuss the various views on God's sovereignty. Remember to major on the majors.

Close in prayer for each other

💜 From Head to Heart

> ~ Truth or Lie Card ~
>
> *Look at the appendix and you will discover your perforated "Truth or Lie" cards. There is one for each of the following weeks. On the front you will write down a lie that you have believed contrary to God's **goodness**. On the back you will find a definition of God's goodness along with the memory verse for this past week. Review it every morning and night. Keep it close for the rest of your life.*

Assignment for Next Week

1. Read chapter 22, "God's Sovereignty," from Tozer's *Knowledge of the Holy* OR read chapter five, "The Sovereignty of God," from my book *God, As He Longs for You to See Him.*

2. Take three minutes each time before you pray this week and count five evidences of God's goodness to you since you last prayed.

3. List the top two struggles/fears in your life and consider what your response should be to these if God is both **good** and **sovereign**.

NOTES

God: As He Longs for You to See Him

4

SESSION FOUR

The Sovereignty of God

"I'd like a drink of water with two parts hydrogen and two parts oxygen, please."

"Sorry, that's hydrogen peroxide—not exactly a thirst quencher."

"Okay, how about one with just two parts hydrogen."

"Well, don't sit near someone smoking."

"Why?"

"You'd be inhaling some highly flammable gas. Ever heard of the Hindenburg?"

"How about three parts hydrogen and one part nitrogen, would that sooth my parched throat?"

"No problem."

"Really?"

"Yeah, if you like ammonia."

Water is defined as two parts hydrogen and one part oxygen. Regardless of personal preferences, scientific credentials, alternative constructs, distaste, or even disdain, you can't change the building blocks of water. Once altered, you have a very different substance.

In our culture's laboratory of tolerance, people want to mix and match their ideas about God and *hope* it turns out to be God. For many, the idea of a *sovereign,* or all-powerful God, cannot be fused with a God who seems to allow free reign on evil. Unfortunately, regardless of personal preferences, scientific credentials, alternative constructs, distaste, or even disdain, you can't change the building blocks of God. Once altered, He ceases to be God.

This week we will discover why tolerance is incompatible with the God portrayed in Scripture. Then we will tackle the apparent contradiction of a God who is both in control and yet permits terror, disaster, and extreme hardship. By the end, we will see why the defining parts of God are both unalterable and trustworthy.

Day 1 ~

Read chapter 5 in *God: As He Longs for You to See Him*.
How did this chapter clear up your view of God's
sovereignty?

Prayer for the Week:

*O sovereign Lord, King
of all creation, Lord of all
that is visible and invisible for all time and eternity, grant that I might
this day allow You to hold
the same place in my
heart that You hold in all
the universe. Teach me to
submit to Your wise
counsel and command
even as the angels of heaven do so with joy and
delight.*

*So fully believe that
You are both good and
sovereign that I would
absolutely refuse to
worry, knowing that You
are working all things for
my good today even those
things I don't understand
and that seem so unfair.*

*O Sovereign Lord, thank
You for Jesus, who by
His willful death and
supernatural resurrection
has defeated death, sin,
and Satan, both now and
forever. I confess You,
Lord Jesus, as my King,
my God, and my faithful
Friend and Savior!*

Amen.

Day 2 ~

Write down a few images that lodge in your mind detailing the grandeur of God.

_____

_____

_____

_____

_____

_____

_____

It's easy to remember those images when life feels grand. But God's *grandness* tends to shrink when life's fault lines shake our world. List the top two struggles/fears in your life and consider what your response should be to these if God is both *good* and *sovereign*.

_____

_____

_____

_____

_____

_____

_____

Thus says the Lord, the King of Israel and his Redeemer, the Lord of hosts:

"I am the first and I am the last, and there is no God besides Me.

"Who is like Me? Let him proclaim and declare it; yes, let him recount it to Me in order, from the time that I established the ancient nation. And let them declare to them the things that are coming and the events that are going to take place. Do not tremble and do not be afraid; Have I not long since announced it to you and declared it? And you are My witnesses is there any God besides Me, or is there any other Rock? I know of none."

— Isaiah 44:6-8

Day 3 ∼
RENEW YOUR MIND

Our vision of who God is can be improved by a clear picture from His Word. Take a moment today to memorize and meditate on these verses:

> *And we know that God causes all things to work together for good to those who love God, to those who are called according to His purpose.*
>
> — Romans 8:28
>
> ════════════════════
>
> *"As for you, you meant evil against me, but God meant it for good in order to bring about this present result, to preserve many people alive."*
>
> — Genesis 50:20

Are you reviewing your Truth or Lie Card? Remember Romans 12:2:

And do not be conformed to this world, but be transformed by the renewing of your mind, so that you may prove what the will of God is, that which is good and acceptable and perfect.

_____
_____
_____
_____
_____
_____
_____
_____
_____
_____
_____
_____

Day 4 ∼

On pages 83-90 of the book, Chip discussed five
ways God has revealed His sovereignty to us. How
have any of those means been apparent in your life?

_____

_____

_____

_____

_____

_____

_____

_____

_____

_____

_____

_____

_____

_____

_____

_____

_____

_____

_____

_____

_____

_____

_____

_____

_____

_____

*"No doubt all history
in the last resort must
be held by Christians
to be a story with a
divine plot."*

— C. S. Lewis

Day 5 ~

Let's get real for a moment. What are you going through that seems hard, unfair, depressing, or impossible? What would it look like to stop fighting, stop resisting, stop complaining, and start trusting your sovereign Father?

_____

_____

_____

_____

_____

_____

_____

_____

_____

_____

_____

_____

_____

_____

Tools for Life Change:

Why do you believe in the God of the Bible? If someone asked you that question would you be able to give a well thought out, logical answer? Could you give an answer without using the Bible as a reference? You may want to listen to the Living on the Edge series, **Why I Believe***, taught by author Chip Ingram which gives genuine answers to questions at the core of human existence.*

An additional resource for future reading is **The Problem of Pain** *by C. S. Lewis.*

DIGGING DEEPER

Read chapter 22
in A. W. Tozer's *Knowledge of the Holy*.

Read chapter 4
in J. I. Packer's *Knowing God*.

"The Sovereinty of God"
Romans 8:28

WATCH VIDEO

INTRODUCTION —
In Flight; Hong Kong to Beijing 1999

Q: What makes you think your god is better than
everyone else's god?

A: Because the God I worship . . .

. . . is <u>before</u> **all** things. Col. 1:17, Ps. 90:2, Rev. 1:8,1 Tim 6:16

. . . <u>created</u> **all** things. Gen. 1:1, Jn. 1:3, Col. 1:16

. . . <u>upholds</u> **all** things. Heb. 1:3, Col. 1:17

. . . is <u>above</u> **all** things. Eph. 4:6, Isa. 45:5-12

. . . <u>knows</u> **all** things. Isa. 46:10, Ps. 139:4, 6

. . . <u>can do</u> **all** things. Jer. 32:27, Lk. 1:37

. . . <u>accomplishes</u> **all** things. Isa. 14:24; 46:10, Eph. 1:11

. . . <u>rules</u> over **all** things. Dan. 4:34-35, 1 Ch. 29:11-12

. . . is in <u>control</u> of **all** things. Job 42:2, Rom. 8:28

> *earthly kings* – Pr. 21:1, Rev. 19:16
>
> *human events* – Dan. 2, 7, Ps. 33:9-11
>
> *good angels* – Col. 1:15-16, Rev. 4:8
>
> *Satan & bad angels* – Job 1:6, Eph. 1:21, Phil. 2:10
>
> *human decisions* – Eph. 1:11, Rom. 8:29-30,
>
> Acts 2:23; 13:48

In a Word, I Worship the Sovereign God of the Universe

I. Defining the Sovereignty of God

Sovereign = *adj.* (1) above or superior to all others; chief; greatest; supreme (2) supreme in power, rank, or authority (3) of or holding the position of ruler; royal; reigning (4) independent of all others (5) excellent; outstanding – *n.* (1) a person who possesses sovereign authority or power; specific, a monarch or ruler

> ~ Synonymous Meaning = *ruler, ultimate authority, "in control," King of kings, Lord of lords, without equal, without limitation in any way, the only absolutely free being in the universe.*

"God's sovereignty is the attribute by which He rules His entire creation, and **to be sovereign God must be all-knowing, all-powerful, and absolutely free**. The reasons are these:

"Were there even one datum of knowledge, however small, unknown to God, His rule would break down at that point. To be Lord over all the creation, He must possess all knowledge. And were God lacking one infinitesimal modicum of power, that lack would end His reign and undo His kingdom; that one stray atom of power would belong to someone else and God would be a limited ruler and hence not sovereign.

Furthermore, His sovereignty requires that He be absolutely free, which means simply that He must be free to do whatever He wills to do anywhere at any time to carry out His eternal purpose in every single detail without interference. Were He less than free He must be less than sovereign."

A. W. Tozer, *Knowledge of the Holy*

II. How Does God Reveal His Sovereignty to Us?

> ~ **Through His Titles**- SOVEREIGN LORD, MOST HIGH, ALPHA & OMEGA, KINGS OF KINGS, LORD OF LORDS

> ~ **Through His Promises**

> > ~ Romans 8:28-30
> > ~ Philippians 2:9-11

～ **Through His <u>Story</u>- History**

    ～ of Israel- Genesis 37-50:20 (Joseph)
    ～ of the Nations- Daniel 2, 7 (4 Kingdoms)

～ **Through <u>Prophecy</u>**- Daniel 2:27, Isaiah 44:6-8 (NLT)

～ **Through <u>Christ</u>**

    ～ His birth- Galatians 4:4, Matthew 2:3-6
    ～ His life (fulfilled hundreds of prophecies)- Mat. 4:14;
    ～ Mat. 12:15-21
    ～ His teaching- John 8:48-58
    ～ His death and resurrection- John 10:17-18
    ～ His ascension and ultimate reign- Acts 1:9-11
                                Rev. 19:11-16

III. <u>Two Questions the Sovereignty of God Raises</u>

If God is sovereign, why did/does He allow evil, pain, and suffering?

If God is sovereign over all people and events in history, doesn't this make a sham of human responsibility?
Romans 9:10–11
Romans 11:33–36

Resources: ***Chosen But Free*** by Norman Geisler
Problem with Pain by C.S. Lewis

IV. <u>How Must We Respond to a Sovereign God?</u>

1. _____ before the King of the universe. Phil. 2:9-11

    Romans 12:1

2. _____ all that comes into your life is either allowed or decreed by a good God who will use it for your benefit. Romans 8:28-29, Genesis 50:20

3. _____ in awe the mystery and majesty of His kind, compassionate, just, and sovereign rule of all that is or will ever be. Romans 11:33-36, Genesis 50:20

    Romans 8:28
    Genesis 50

Small Group Questions

1. Share a time around the group when you or someone you know experienced a "raw deal" that seemed terrible but ended up as something wonderful.

_____

_____

2. Share one new truth about the sovereignty of God that you've learned through this study.

_____

_____

3. Share one area in your life that you know God wants you to totally surrender. What next steps do you need to take for Him to be the CEO of your life?

_____

_____

 From Head to Heart

> ## ～ Truth or Lie Card ～
> *Look at the appendix and you will discover your perforated "Truth or Lie" cards. There is one for each week. On the front you will write down a lie that you have believed contrary to God's sovereignty. On the back you will find a definition of God's **sovereignty** along with the memory verse for this past week. Review it every morning and night. Keep it close for the rest of your life.*

Assignment for Next Week

Read chapter 6 from God as He Longs or chapter 21 from The Knowledge of the Holy.

NOTES

God: As He Longs for You to See Him

SESSION FIVE

The Holiness of God

One wrong turn can make all the difference.

Have you ever been given a list of directions only to discover at one crossroad you forgot to write down an "R" or an "L"? You have a choice. You can either make a phone call to discover the right way to go. Or, as most of us do, you can make a guess based upon your gut feeling. Unfortunately, if we make the wrong turn, just to get back on the right road, we end up taking time, energy, not to mention hearing a slew of "Brilliant! Now you've gone and gotten us lost!"

When we approach the word *holy*, we have a choice to make. We can pick up the Bible and discover what the word means. Or, as most of us do, we can make a guess based upon our gut feeling of what the word means and how it is applied to God. Unfortunately, if we take the wrong turn, we are absolutely clueless as to what Peter could mean by the phrase, "You shall be holy, for I am holy." Does that mean we need to be *perfect? Innocent? Pure?* Man, who can travel down that road?

When we say God is holy, or when we say He wants us to be holy, what do we mean? This week we will learn how we have mislabeled "holiness" as it concerns God. Words like *perfect, pure,* and *innocent* are good guesses, but in reality they take us down a wrong road in our understanding of God. In our assumptions, we've stripped God of the essence of His holiness. God longs for you to see Him as He is, not as we would want Him to be. This week, let's discover the right turn.

Day 1 ~

Read chapter 6 in *God: As He Longs for You to See Him*.
How did this chapter clear up your view of God's
holiness?

_____
_____
_____
_____
_____
_____
_____
_____
_____
_____
_____
_____
_____
_____
_____
_____
_____
_____
_____
_____
_____
_____
_____
_____

Prayer for the Week:

*O Lord God, holy and
pure, awesome in majesty,
as I consider Your perfection, grant that I might
commit to holy ways,
think holy thoughts,
live in holy obedience,
and reject evil with a
holy attitude.*

*Let me hear the tender
conviction of Your Spirit
and help me remember
that You are jealous for
Your holiness. Because of
Your love, You see the
pain our sin will bring us,
and You long to rescue us.
So that Your name may
never be profaned in my
life, You have my permis-
sion to do whatever You
need to do to make be
holy.*

In Jesus' name,

Amen.

Day 2 ~

How does seeing God as "totally other" help us view ourselves in more realistic light?

_____

_____

_____

_____

_____

_____

_____

_____

And one called out to
another and said,

"Holy, Holy, Holy,
is the Lord of hosts,
the whole earth is
full of His glory."

— Isaiah 6:3

Pursue peace with all
men, and the sanctifica-
tion without which no
one will see the Lord.

— Hebrews 12:14

Read 1 Corinthians 3:17. Explain why living a holy life is so important to God. How do His commands reveal His love for us and His desire for our wholeness and health?

_____

_____

_____

_____

_____

_____

_____

_____

_____

_____

_____

Day 3 ⁓

RENEW YOUR MIND

Our vision of who God is can be improved by a clear picture from His Word. Take a moment today to memorize and meditate on these verses:

> *As obedient children, do not be conformed to the former lusts which were yours in your ignorance, but like the Holy One who called you, be holy yourselves also in all your behavior; because it is written, "You shall be holy, for I am holy."*
>
> — I Peter 1:14-16

REMINDER

Are you reviewing your Truth or Lie Card?

Day 4 ~

Look up Ephesians 4:17-24. In that passage Paul contrasts our life before Christ and our life after Christ. Unfortunately, many Christians think they can follow Christ without looking any different.

Meditate on those verses and then take some time with the chart below. First write out the three commands from Paul found in Ephesians 4:22-24. Then, commit to one application in each area.

"Holy is the way God is. To be holy He does not conform to a standard. He is that standard."

— A. W. Tozer

Imperatives	Applied to My Life

Day 5 ~

Look back over pages 118-123 in the book. Chip talked about four key ways that we grow in holiness: *a commitment, the way we think, a command, or an attitude.* Which of the four do you need to work on most and why? Pray for the wisdom and power of God's Spirit for life change.

_____

_____

_____

_____

_____

_____

_____

_____

_____

_____

_____

Tools for
Life Change:

The following
resources may be
helpful during your
study from author
Chip Ingram. These
materials can be
purchased at
www.Livingonthe
Edge.org.

*The Miracle of
Life Change*

Read chapter 21
in A. W. Tozer's *Knowledge of the Holy.*

"The Holiness of God"
Hebrews 12:14

I.   Defining the Holiness of God

"We know nothing like the divine holiness. It stands apart, unique, unapproachable, incomprehensible and unattainable. The natural man is blind to it. He may fear God's power and admire His wisdom, but His holiness he cannot even imagine."

A. W. Tozer, *Knowledge of the Holy*

~ Root Word = to divide, to mark off, to set apart from all else; it's the opposite of <u>profane</u> – or to be common or ordinary – to be holy is to be <u>different</u>, <u>distinct</u>, or <u>unique</u> from the common or ordinary.

~ The Holiness of God is that which divides Him from everyone and everything else. It is the quality of God being different, distinct, unique – one of a kind.

Who among the gods is like you, O LORD?
Who is like you—
majestic in holiness,
awesome in glory,
working wonders?
Exodus 15:11 (NIV)

~ God's Holiness refers to both His <u>majesty</u> and <u>moral purity</u>. Holiness is the absolute absence of evil (1 John 1:5) and encompasses and defines all that is pure, whole, righteous, and healthy in the universe.

II. How Does God Reveal His Holiness to Us?

~ **Through People** – Moses' Life (Exodus 3),
David's Sin (2 Samuel 11),
Isaiah's Crisis (Isaiah 6)

~ **Through Places** – Burning Bush, Red Sea, Tabernacle,
Solomon's Temple, The Church
Gathered Acts 3:23-31), Heaven
(Revelation 4)

~ **Through the Law** – 10 Commandments (Exodus 20),
Leviticus, Deuteronomy

~ **Through the Prophets** – Samuel, Jonah, Isaiah, Jeremiah
and Zechariah

~ **Through His Wrath
and Judgment** – O.T. Achan (Joshua 7), N.T. Ananias &
Sapphira (Acts 5), Israel's Diaspora
(Nehemiah 1), The Church Disciplined
(1 Corinthians 11)

~ **Through His Son**
  ~ a holy birth – Isaiah 7:14
  ~ a holy life – John 8:46
  ~ a holy sneak preview – Mark 9:2-10
  ~ an unholy death – 2 Corinthians 5:21
  ~ a holy resurrection – John 20:26-31
  ~ a holy ascension – Hebrews 4:14-16
  ~ a holy priesthood – Hebrews 9:11-28

~ **Through His Church** – Gathered (1 Corinthians 3:16),
Scattered (1 Corinthians 6:18-20)

III. God's Holiness Raises Two Important Questions

1. If God is so holy that He cannot even gaze at sin, how can sinful people like us have a relationship with Him?

2. If trusting in Christ's work on the cross blots out our sin before God and we are holy in His sight, why do we keep on sinning?

    1. Justification – positional holiness (our position with God)

    2. Sanctification – progressive holiness (making progress)

    3. Glorification – permanently holy (like Him)

IV. How Must We Respond to the Holiness of God?

It's a _____ we make.   Hebrews 12:14

It's a _____ that we think.   Ephesians 4:17-24
                                                          Romans 12:2

It's a _____ we obey.   1 Peter 1:14-16
                                                          Hebrews 13:4

It's an _____ we develop.   Proverbs 8:13
                                                          2 Corinthians 6:14-7:1

Small Group Questions

1. In the book we talked about the two areas we struggle with the most: sex and money. Where do you believe you are at right now? What step does God want you to take in each area?

2. What is the biggest barrier to taking that step of obedience today?

3. Who could help you and hold you accountable to take those steps towards holiness?

 From Head to Heart

> ### ~ Truth or Lie Card ~
>
> *Look at the appendix and you will discover your perforated "Truth or Lie" cards. There is one for each week. On the front you will write down a lie that you have believed contrary to God's **holiness.** On the back you will find a definition of God's holiness along with the memory verse for this past week. Review it every morning and night. Keep it close for the rest of your life.*

Assignment for Next Week

Read Chapter 7 on The Wisdom of God.

Remember to work through your journal.

For more information on the teaching series The Miracle of Life Change click on www.Living ontheEdge.org/smallgroup

---

FACILITATOR T!PS

If the group is mixed, please separate genders before you get started on the questions.

Look for opportunities to follow up with people in the group this week in light of the struggles they have shared.

Spend some extra time in prayer for each person.

God: As He Longs for You to See Him

6

SESSION SIX

The Wisdom of God

Nothing intrigues us like mystery.

Except when it *really* happens.

Our eyes leap over pages of a "whodunit." We flock to the big screen when we hear, "You won't believe the ending!" Why? Because we love when a mystery is unveiled and then resolved. Think about the flip side. We let out a moan when the words flash across our favorite TV show, "To be continued." Who likes to leave a stadium in a tie? And that doesn't come close to the feelings that pound us in real-life thrillers:

> ∼ As we wait to find out if the chemo treatments will halt the cancer
>
> ∼ As we wonder why the pink slip hit our desk
>
> ∼ As we watch the hurricane move closer to shore

Mystery unveiled: *tantalizing.*

Mystery unresolved: *frustrating.*

When theologians describe the simplicity of God, they mean that all of His perfect attributes work perfectly together, in simple harmony. We describe with great clarity His perfect love married with His perfect justice and His perfect holiness. But we trip over our minds when we try to figure out how He is also perfect in His mystery. The preacher of Ecclesiastes asks rhetorically, "Consider the work of God, for who is able to straighten what He has bent?" (Ecclesiastes 7:13). The picture is one of bare hands trying to straighten curved steel.

What sweat and tears have you lost on trying to straighten out your circumstances? What temples have you rubbed raw trying to figure out how God is going to use this dreadful experience? Surely God can't know about this situation. Doesn't He see how crooked my life is? Why doesn't He straighten it out?

This week we will learn why living in "to be continued" land is not only a necessity, but actually the best thing for us. We will be introduced to another of God's attributes: His wisdom. And that's not about God's IQ. When stuck in your next unresolved mystery, remember these principles on how we can learn to *rest* and *trust* in the wisdom of God.

Day I ~

Read chapter 7 in *God: As He Longs for You to See Him.*
How did this chapter clear up your view of God's
wisdom?

Prayer for the Week:

*O Lord God, infinite in
wisdom and knowledge, as
I consider Your purposes
and Your plans, grant that
I might*

*Live in total awe and
reverence for You, feast
daily upon Your Word, ask
for Your wisdom in every
situation, and trust You
completely when life
doesn't make sense.*

*Let me know Your will
and help me to follow
it wholeheartedly,
remembering that You
already know every ripple
of every action throughout
history, now and forever.
Because of Your wisdom,
You freely offer Your best
in every situation, and You
provide it to all who ask.
So today, I ask.*

In Jesus' name,

Amen.

Day 2 ~

Look at the verse on this page. In light of what you have read this week about how God has revealed his wisdom, how does Scripture prove that point?

"For My thoughts are not your thoughts, Nor are your ways My ways," _declares the Lord. "For as the heavens are higher than the earth, so are My ways higher than your ways and My thoughts than your thoughts."_

— Isaiah 55:8-9

Day 3 ～

RENEW YOUR MIND

Our vision of who God is can be improved by a
clear picture from His Word. Take a moment
today to memorize and meditate
on these verses:

> *Oh, the depth of the riches both of the wisdom
> and knowledge of God! How unsearchable are
> His judgments and unfathomable His ways! For
> who has known the mind of the Lord, or who
> became His counselor? Or who has first given to
> Him that it might be paid back to Him again?
> For from Him and through Him and to Him are
> all things to Him be the glory forever. Amen.*
>
> — Romans 11:33-36

Are you reviewing
your Truth or
Lie Card?

_____

_____

_____

_____

_____

_____

_____

_____

_____

_____

Day 4 ～

Imagine a time in your life when you were in the
midst of a great struggle. Maybe you are presently in
one of those whirlpools. Now that you have a greater
grasp on the wisdom of God, ponder how you may
view that struggle through the lens of God's wisdom.
How can you learn to rest and trust in His wisdom?

*"The real basis of
wisdom is a frank
acknowledgment that
this world's course is
enigmatic, that much
of what happens is
quite inexplicable to us,
and that most occur-
rences "under the sun"
bear no outward sign of
a rational, moral God
ordering them at all."*

— J. I. Packer

Day 5 ～

Let's get real for a moment. What are you going through that seems hard, unfair, depressing, or impossible? What would it look like to stop fighting, stop resisting, stop complaining, and start trusting your sovereign Father?

_____

_____

_____

_____

_____

_____

_____

_____

_____

_____

_____

_____

_____

_____

_____

_____

_____

_____

_____

_____

_____

_____

_____

"The Wisdom of God"

WATCH VIDEO

I.   <u>How Has God Revealed His Wisdom to Us?</u>

    ～ **Through <u>Creation</u>** – Psalm 19:1-7, Psalm 104:24

    ～ **Through <u>Providence</u>** – Psalm 33:10-11, Romans 8:28

    ～ **Through <u>Redemption</u>** – 1 Corinthians 2:6-10

"God's almighty wisdom is always active, and never fails. All His works of creation and providence and grace display it, and until we can see it in them we just are not seeing them straight. **But we cannot recognize God's wisdom unless we know the end for which He is working**... God's wisdom is not, and never was, pledged to keep a fallen world happy, or to make ungodliness comfortable. Not even to Christians has He promised a trouble-free life; rather the reverse. He has other ends in view for life in this world than simply to make it easy for everyone.

What is He after, then? What is His goal? What does He aim at?... He plans that a great host of mankind should come to love and honor Him. **His ultimate objective is to bring them to a state in which they please Him entirely and praise Him adequately, a state in which He is all in all to them, and He and they rejoice continually in the knowledge of each other's love** – men rejoicing in the saving love of God, set upon them from all eternity, and God rejoicing in the responsive love of men, drawn out of them by grace through the gospel."

J.I. Packer, *Knowing God*

    ～ **Through His <u>Son</u>** – 1 Corinthians 1:30, James 3:17

II. How Must We Respond to the Wisdom of God?

～ We must learn to ＿＿＿＿＿＿＿wisely!

Ephesians 5:15-17

HOW?

1. It begins with ＿＿＿＿＿＿for God.

Proverbs 1:7, Job 28:28

2. It grows with ＿＿＿＿＿＿＿His Word.

Psalm 119:97-100, 2 Timothy 3:15-17

3. It ＿＿＿＿＿＿ asking for it specifically.

James 1:5, Colossians 1:9

4. We must learn to ＿＿＿＿＿＿＿completely; that all that comes our way is from the hand of a <u>good</u> and <u>loving</u> God who <u>knowing</u> all things actual and possible, is exerting His unlimited <u>power</u> to execute the **best possible outcomes** by the **best possible means** to fulfill the **highest possible purposes**.

Assignment for Spiritual Growth

1. Sit quietly for 15 minutes and ponder your most difficult circumstance through the lens of God's wisdom.
2. Read J. I. Packer's *Knowing God* chapter ten, focusing especially on pages 93-97 which offers valuable insight into our purpose in life and how to live it. This is the <u>finest overview of Ecclesiastes</u> that I've ever come across.

Small Group Questions

1. What is the toughest issue you're facing in your life right now (that you feel safe enough to share)?

2. What did you learn about God's wisdom that gave you hope or comfort?

3. What practical steps are you currently taking to gain God's wisdom? What are your best practices?

 From Head to Heart

> ### ～ Truth or Lie Card ～
>
> *Look at the appendix and you will discover your perforated "Truth or Lie" cards. There is one for each week. On the front you will write down a lie that you have believed contrary to God's wisdom. On the back you will find a definition of God's **wisdom** along with the memory verse for this past week. Review it every morning and night. Keep it close for the rest of your life.*

Assignment for Next Week

Read Chapter 8, work through your journal and review the truth/lie cards.

NOTES

God: As He Longs for You to See Him

7

SESSION SEVEN

The Justice of God

Have you ever seen a dog with a shock collar?

Once he strays outside predetermined boundaries, the collar shocks, the dog yelps, and the masochistic among us chuckle.

He breaks the law. He receives immediate justice. Wouldn't it be nice if that would work in our world? Let's rephrase that: Wouldn't it be nice if that would work in our world for everyone except me? Instead, it appears like so many dogs are running loose.

We wonder about God's justice when we hear of the missionary family who moves to an unreached tribe only for the mom to contract a terminal disease. And on the flip side, our fairness needle pushes to the limit when we think about the thugs of society getting off scot-free and in the process, driving a corvette. Our skeptical preacher in Ecclesiastes laments, "I have seen everything during my lifetime of futility; there is a righteous man who perishes in his righteousness and there is a wicked man who prolongs his life in his wickedness" (Ecclesiastes 7:15).

Someone has said, "God must love wicked people, because He puts up with so many of them." We all have heard that God is both just and fair, but this week we will ask why, in our world, bad things happen to good people, and what's even more frustrating, good things happen to bad people. We then learn some practical ways to relax when we wonder why God allows so many dogs to run loose.

Day 1 ～

Read chapter 8 in *God: As He Longs for You to See Him*. How did this chapter clear up your view of God's justice?

Prayer for the Week:

O Lord God, holy and just, as I consider Your righteous judgments, grant that I might learn to treasure the sacrifice and atonement of Jesus, abandon all vengeance to You and refuse to seek it on my own terms, take comfort in You when life is unfair, and remember that I will one day stand before Your judgment seat.

Help me to rest in Your righteousness and defer to Your justice. Because You are Judge of all the earth, I bow patiently before Your authority in faith and in gratitude.

In Jesus' name,

Amen.

Day 2 ~

Reread the questions on pages 151-152. Which one do you struggle with the most and why? How has this chapter helped resolve any tension or shed light on your appreciation of God's justice?

Clouds and thick darkness surround Him; righteousness and justice are the foundation of His throne.

— Psalm 97: 2

_____

_____

_____

_____

_____

_____

_____

_____

_____

_____

_____

_____

_____

_____

_____

_____

_____

_____

_____

_____

_____

_____

Day 3 〜

RENEW YOUR MIND

Our vision of who God is can be improved by a clear picture from His Word. Take a moment today to memorize and meditate on these verses:

> *Never pay back evil for evil to anyone. Respect what is right in the sight of all men. If possible, so far as it depends on you, be at peace with all men. Never take your own revenge, beloved, but leave room for the wrath of God, for it is written, "Vengeance is mine, I will repay," says the Lord. "But if your enemy is hungry, feed him, and if he is thirsty, give him a drink; for in so doing you will heap burning coals on his head." Do not be overcome by evil, but overcome evil with good.*
>
> — Romans 12: 17-21

Are you reviewing your Truth or Lie Cards?

Day 4 ~

Pilots will tell you that as little as one-eighth inch of ice covering a wing can prevent a plane from taking off. Imagine that, a massive, steel bird with big turbine engines grounded because of a thin sheet of ice.

In the same way, many of us are grounded in our life because of a thin veneer of bitterness covering our hearts. Jesus said in Matthew:

"And his lord, moved with anger, handed him over to the torturers until he should repay all that was owed him.
My heavenly Father will also do the same to you, if each of you does not forgive his brother from your heart."

— Matthew 18:34-35

Take a few moments to ask yourself:

~ Is there anyone I hold stuff against,
  even a little bit?

~ Is there anyone I secretly talk about?

~ Is there anyone I'd love to see God judge now so I
  can experience their humiliation?

It's time to de-ice your heart. Let the Father take care of justice. Meditate on **Psalm 73** and seek forgiveness for the bitterness in your own heart.

> *"There are two kinds of people: those who say to God, "Thy will be done," and those to whom God says, "All right, then, have it your way."*
>
> — C. S. Lewis

Day 5 ~

Read 1 Peter 3:8-17 and 4:12-19. What are some practical ways for believers to find freedom from bitterness?

_____

_____

_____

_____

_____

_____

_____

_____

_____

_____

_____

_____

_____

_____

_____

_____

_____

_____

_____

Read chapter 17
in A. W. Tozer's _Knowledge of the Holy._

Read chapter 14
in J. I. Packer's _Knowing God._

"The Justice of God"
Genesis 18:25

WATCH VIDEO

I.   Defining "The Justice of God"

~ Revealed through Abraham – Genesis 18:25 (NIV)

"Far be it from you to do such a thing—to kill the righteous
with the wicked, treating the righteous and the wicked alike. Far
be it from you! Will not the Judge of all the earth do right?"

~ Revealed through the Psalmist – Psalm 97:2 (NIV)

"Clouds and thick darkness surround him; righteousness and
justice are the foundation of his throne."

~ "Justice embodies the idea of moral equity, and iniquity is the
exact opposite; it is *in*-equity, the absence of equality from
human thoughts and acts. Judgment is the application of equity to moral situations and may be favorable or unfavorable
according to whether the one under examination has been equi-
table or inequitable in heart and conduct."

A. W. Tozer, *Knowledge of the Holy*

~ "...it becomes clear that the Bible's proclamation of God's work
as Judge is part of its witness to His character . . . It shows us
also that the heart of the justice which expresses God's nature
is retribution, the rendering to men, what they have deserved;
for this is the essence of the judge's task. To reward good with
good, and evil with evil, is natural to God. So, when the New
Testament speaks of the final judgment, it always represents it
in terms of retribution. God will judge all men, it says,
'according to their works' (Matthew 16:27; Revelation
20:12f)."

J. I. Packer, *Knowing God*

II. How Does God Reveal His Justice to Us?

~ Through the <u>Natural</u> Order – Romans 1:18-20

~ Through the <u>Human Heart</u> – Romans 2:15-16; Acts 28:3-6

~ "These, then are the two points I wanted to make. First, that human beings, all over the earth, have this curious idea that they ought to behave in a certain way, and cannot really get rid of it. Secondly, that they do not in fact behave in that way. They know the Law of Nature; they break it. These two facts are the foundation of all clear thinking about ourselves and the universe we live in."

C. S. Lewis

~ Through His Role as <u>Judge</u> – Hebrews 12:23;
2 Timothy 4:8; John 5:22-ff

~ Through the <u>Cross</u> – Romans 3:25-26 (NIV)

[25]God presented him as a sacrifice of atonement, through faith in his blood. He did this to demonstrate his justice, because in his forbearance he had left the sins committed beforehand unpunished— [26]he did it to demonstrate his justice at the present time, so as to be just and the one who justifies those who have faith in Jesus.

~ Through the Promise of <u>Eternal</u> <u>Retribution</u>

~ For Believers – 1 Corinthians 3:10-15

~ For Unbelievers – Hebrews 9:27

III. How Are We to Respond to God's Justice?

~ _____ to embrace Jesus today as your Savior rather
than meet Him as your righteous judge later.

John 5:22-24

~ _____ to take revenge when treated unjustly knowing
God and God alone is judge.

Romans 12:17-21

~ _____ when you encounter injustice knowing God will
"balance the scales" either in this life or the next.   Psalm 73

Take comfort in God's justice.

~ _____ deeply on the reality of the "judgment seat of
Christ," the promise of spiritual reward and loss.

2 Corinthians 5:10;
1 Corinthians 3:10-15

Meditate on the effects of God's judgement.

Small Group Questions

1. Share a time when you've questioned God's justice, either in your life or in the life of a person you love.

2. What did you learn about God's justice in this study to help you cope in the midst of the situation?

3. Which of the four responses to God's justice resonates most with you in your life right now? Why?

   Four responses:
   1. *Choose to embrace Jesus.*
   2. *Refuse to seek vengeance.*
   3. *Take comfort in God's justice.*
   4. *Meditate on the effects of God's final judgment.*

4. Is there a specific action step you need to take in response to God's justice? If so, write it down and then share it with the group or a close friend.

 From Head to Heart

> ### ∼ Truth or Lie Card ∼
>
> *Look at the appendix and you will discover your perforated "Truth or Lie" cards. There is one for each week. On the front you will write down a lie that you have believed contrary to God's **justice**. On the back you will find a definition of God's justice along with the memory verse for this past week. Review it every morning and night. Keep it close for the rest of your life.*

Assignment for Next Week

Read Chapter 9

God: As He Longs for You to See Him

8

SESSION EIGHT

The Love of God

You know what happens when you leave soda out on the counter for a few hours.

Overexposure leads to flatness.

The same thing happens with the word *love.* Love. I love shopping. I love burgers. I love my team. I love that song. I love my bride. I love my kids. I love my dog. Overexposure leads to flatness.

The word *love* is like a conversational Swiss army knife—perfect for any situation. We apply it as easily to cooked cow as we do our groom of 50 years. We use it affectionately for our daughters and ardently for our favorite football team.

What does God's love look like? Feel like? Has its flavor fallen flat on you? For many of us, we react to the knowledge of God's love as we do the tax code—a cold fact of life. Especially those of us who have been in the church for any length of time, the mantra "God loves you" moved from humbling to humdrum years ago.

God wants to move us back from flat to flavorful. We will come to realize that most of the problem stems from our lack of belief in His love. We know it in our mind, but never feel it in our heart. In the process we will discover five truths of what God's love means for us that will not only change how we view God's love, but may change how we love others.

Day 1 ~

Read chapter 9 in *God: As He Longs for You to See Him*.
How did this chapter clear up your view of
God's love?

_____

_____

_____

_____

_____

_____

_____

_____

_____

_____

_____

_____

_____

_____

_____

_____

_____

_____

_____

_____

_____

_____

_____

Prayer for the Week:

O Lord, the God who is love, as I consider the infinite nature of Your compassion, mercy, and favor, grant that I might grasp and accept the reality of Your love, abandon all the things I've tried to use as substitutes, and sacrificially demonstrate Your love to others.

Let me rely on and rest in the certainty of Your unconditional love, even when I don't feel it. Help me to see it even in difficult times, to know that it's always there regardless of my performance, and to thank You for it constantly. Let it really sink into my heart as I've never known it before.

In Jesus' name,

Amen.

Day 2 ∼

On page 184, Chip asks the question, "What would my life feel like and be like if I really believed God thinks of me in this way?" He then lists five implications of God's love for us. Which of the five did you need to hear today and why?

See how great a love the Father has bestowed on us, that we would be called children of God; and such we are for this reason the world does not know us, because it did not know Him.

— I John 3:1

Day 3 ∾
RENEW YOUR MIND

Our vision of who God is can be improved by a clear picture from His Word. Take a moment today to memorize and meditate on these verses:

> *For I am convinced that neither death, nor life, nor angels, nor principalities, nor things present, nor things to come, nor powers, nor height, nor depth, nor any other created thing, will be able to separate us from the love of God, which is in Christ Jesus our Lord.*
>
> — Romans 8:38-39

Are you reviewing your Truth or Lie Cards?

Day 4 ~

Fill in the blank: I tend to believe that I earn God's love if I _____. What prevents you from knowing God's love in your mind, and gives you a tough time experiencing it in your heart?

_____

_____

_____

_____

_____

_____

_____

_____

_____

_____

_____

_____

_____

_____

_____

"The change of which I speak is the change from living life as a painful test to prove that you deserve to be loved, to living it as an unceasing "Yes" to the truth of that Belovedness."

— Henri Nouwen

DIGGING DEEPER

Read chapter 20
in A. W. Tozer's *Knowledge of the Holy.*

Read chapter 12
in J. I. Packer's *Knowing God.*

Day 5 ～

How are you receiving God's love in your mind? As an afterthought or a forethought? Instead of receiving His love by faith, we tend to settle for tangible, and temporal, replacements. C. S. Lewis aptly affirmed,

> Indeed, if we consider the unblushing promises of reward and the staggering nature of the rewards promised in the Gospels, it would seem that our Lord finds our desire, not too strong, but too weak. We are half-hearted creatures, fooling about with drink and sex and ambition when infinite joy is offered us, like an ignorant child who wants to go on making mud pies in a slum because he cannot imagine what is meant by the offer of a holiday at the sea. We are far too easily pleased.

Take your journal out and ask yourself, "How am I replacing God's love with cheap substitutes?" Is it more stuff? Puffed up ego? Unhealthy relationships?

Ask for God to help you grasp His love for you. Commit to never be lured again by your own "mud pies." *Extra writing pages are provided on next couple of pages.

_____
_____
_____
_____
_____
_____
_____
_____
_____
_____

Tools for Life Change:

Do you know that you are precious to God? You are fully forgiven, deeply loved and have great worth, regardless of your past, childhood, mistakes and choices. You have great worth because of your relationship with Christ. We all spend many hours and days trying to be someone significant, only to realize we often don't like the person we see in the mirror. Chip's wife, Theresa Ingram, has an excellent CD series, **Precious in His Sight**, which will help you to see yourself through the eyes of Jesus. This resource is available at Living on the Edge or you can purchase it by logging on to www.Livingonthe Edge.org.

"The Love of God"
John 3:16

 WATCH VIDEO

Three Facts about Love

Fact #1:   **IT'S A <u>UNIVERSAL</u> <u>NEED</u>** = We are all looking for love!

Fact #2:   **THERE'S A <u>UNIVERSAL SOLUTION</u>** = God loves all people everywhere and longs to meet the deepest needs of their heart for love!

Fact #3:   **THERE'S A <u>TRAGIC DISCONNECTION</u>** = Nevertheless, most people remain starved for love for three primary reasons:

1. They don't <u>know</u> God loves them.
2. They know of God's love, but have <u>not received</u> it.
3. They have received God's love, but don't know how to <u>experience</u> it in daily life.

"Over the years, I have come to realize that the greatest trap in our life is not success, popularity, or power, but self-rejection. Success, popularity, and power can indeed present a great temptation, **but their seductive quality often comes from the way they are part of the much larger temptation to self-rejection.** When we have come to believe in the voices that call us worthless and unlovable, then success, popularity, and power are easily perceived as attractive solutions. The real trap, however, is self-rejection... *Self-rejection is the greatest enemy of the spiritual life* because it contradicts the sacred voice that calls us the 'Beloved.' **Being the Beloved constitutes the core truth of our existence.**"

Henry Nouwen

(As quoted in Brennan Manning's, *Abba's Child*)

I. Defining "The Love of God"

⁓ **Definition** – God's love is His holy disposition toward all that He has created that compels Him to express unconditional affection and selective correction to provide the highest and best quality of existence both now and forever for the objects of His love.

⁓ **God's love for you means . . .**

1. His thoughts, intentions, desires, and plans for you are always for your good and never for your harm.

2. He is kind, open, approachable, frank, and eager to be your friend.

3. He emotionally identifies with your pain, joy, hopes, and dreams and has chosen to allow your happiness to affect His own.

4. He takes pleasure in you just for who you are totally apart from your performance and/or accomplishments.

5. He is actively and creatively orchestrating people, circumstances, and events to express His affection and selective correction to provide for your highest good.

⁓ **Characteristics of God's agape love include:**

⁓ It is a <u>giving</u> love – John 3:16
⁓ It is a <u>sacrificial</u> love – John 3:16
⁓ It is an <u>unconditional</u> love – John 3:16
⁓ It is a <u>boundless</u> love – Ephesians 3:14-21

⁓ **God's love is expressed primarily through His <u>goodness</u>, <u>mercy</u>, <u>longsuffering</u>, and <u>grace</u>.**

Ryrie's Basic Theology (p. 44)

II. **God <u>Reveals</u> His Love to Us Through . . .**
See page 186.

_____ - He <u>made</u> you for Himself.
Genesis 1:26-27, Colossians 1:16

_____ - He shows His <u>kindness</u> to all.
Matthew 5:44-45, Acts 17:24-27

_____ - He is proactively <u>pursuing</u> you.
Luke 19:10, John 4:23-24

_____ - He <u>chastises</u> us to protect us from
self-destructive behavior.
Hebrews 12:6

_____ - He supernaturally <u>pours</u> His love into our
hearts by the Holy Spirit.
Romans 5:5

_____ - Jesus revealed the <u>nature</u> of God's love for us.

∽ Jesus' **life** <u>modeled</u> compassion, grace, and truth – John 1:14

∽ Jesus' **teaching** <u>explained</u> God's love– Luke 15

∽ Jesus' **death** <u>demonstrated</u> the extent of God's love – 1 John
3:16, Romans 5:8

"But God demonstrates his own love for us in this: While we were still sinners, Christ died for us."
Romans 5:8 (NIV)

---

*An object's value is always determined by the price paid for it.
To God, you are worth the price of His Son's death in your place.

III. How Must We Respond to God's Love?

～ We must _____ faith in **our hearts**.

John 3:16, John 1:12

"Yet to all who received him, to those who believed in his name, he gave the right to become children of God."

John 1:12

～ We must _____ it by faith in **our minds**.

1 John 4:13-16

HOW?

1. Saturate your mind in the truth of God's love for you.

Romans 8:38-39

2. Ask God to help you grasp His love for you.

Ephesians 3:14-21

3. Refuse to seek love in cheap substitutes.

1 John 2:15-16

～ We must _____ it by faith through **our wills**.

～ The command – John 13:34-35
～ The calling – 1 John 3:16-18
～ The promise – Luke 6:38

Resources:
～ Tozer's, *Knowledge of the Holy* – chapter 20
～ Packer's, *Knowing God* – chapter 12
～ Theresa Ingram, CD Series, *How Great A Love* (SCBC 2002 Women's Retreat) LivingontheEdge.org

FACILITATOR T!PS

Close your time with prayer.

Most believers struggle with experiencing the love of God. Look out for those that may need extra reminders in the coming weeks.

Make sure everyone has an accountability partner to help take those steps of obedience.

Small Group Questions

1. Share a time when you've felt deeply loved by God. Why?

2. What is your biggest barrier in believing and receiving God's love for you?

3. What specific steps of faith/obedience are you going to take to help you experience and enjoy God's unconditional love for you?

 From Head to Heart

[
~ Truth or Lie Card ~

*Look at the appendix and you will discover your perforated "Truth or Lie" cards. There is one for each week. On the front you will write down a lie that you have believed contrary to God's love. On the back you will find a definition of God's **love** along with the memory verse for this past week. Review it every morning and night. Keep it close for the rest of your life.*
]

Assignment for Next Week

Read Chapter 10 and complete the daily journal entries.

God: As He Longs for You to See Him

9

SESSION NINE

The Faithfulness of God

The second law of thermodynamics states:

The total entropy of any thermodynamically isolated system tends to increase over time, approaching a maximum value.

And all God's people said, "Huh??" In English: Everything in the universe is gradually deteriorating. Practically speaking, that means light bulbs burn out. Batteries run down. Cars rust out. Bodies wear out. Friends move away. Homes fall apart. And we put caskets in the ground.

It appears so much of our time is spent replacing, maintaining, preventing, and mourning. If everything is in a state of deterioration, what in this world can we count on to remain the same?

Nothing created. But it appears the second law of thermodynamics doesn't apply to the Creator. He never burns out, runs down, rusts out, wears out, moves away, falls apart, or dies. Biblically we call Him the Alpha and the Omega, the beginning and the end, the One who was, and is, and is to come. In a word, *faithful.* God's faithfulness can be defined as His constant and "loyal love" for us.

Max Lucado writes about God's faithful love to us:

> *Father, Your love never ceases. Never. Though we spurn you, ignore You, disobey You, You will not change. Our evil cannot diminish Your love. Our goodness cannot increase it. Our faith does not earn it anymore than our stupidity jeopardizes it. You don't love us less if we fail. You don't love us more if we succeed.*

This week we will discover why God is the only Person in the universe we can count on. His faithfulness has been revealed through the centuries. His faithfulness bolsters us with hope when the repair bills come in, the mirror stops flattering, and tombstones dot the landscape of our lives.

Day 1 ~

Read chapter 10 in *God: As He Longs for You to See Him*. How did this chapter clear up your view of God's faithfulness?

Prayer for the Week:

O Lord, my faithful, unfailing God, as I consider Your faithfulness and remember its newness each and every morning, grant that I might put all my sin behind me, covered by Your faithfulness to forgive, bring every detail of every problem to You, abandon all false hopes and place all my hope in You, and be zealous to tell of Your faithfulness

Let the certainty of Your faithfulness sink into my heart. Help me always to trust that You will come through 100 percent of the time in every situation, now and forever.

In Jesus' name,

Amen.

Day 2 ~

How has God proven faithful to you throughout your life?

It is a trustworthy statement: For if we died with Him, we will also live with Him; if we endure, we will also reign with Him; if we deny Him, He also will deny us; if we are faithless, He remains faithful, for He cannot deny Himself.

— 2 Timothy 2:11-13

Day 3 ~
RENEW YOUR MIND

Our vision of who God is can be improved by a clear picture from His Word. Take a moment today to memorize and meditate on these verses:

This I recall to my mind, therefore I have hope. The Lord's lovingkindnesses indeed never cease, for His compassions never fail. They are new every morning; great is Your faithfulness. "The Lord is my portion," says my soul, "Therefore I have hope in Him."

— Lamentations 3:21-24

Are you reviewing your Truth or Lie Cards?

Day 4 ～

Open up to 2 Corinthians 12:9-10. What has been a thorn in your life? How has God shaped you through the pain?

_Great is Thy
faithfulness,
O God my Father
There is no shadow of
turning with Thee;
Thou changest not,
Thy compassions
they fail not;
As Thou hast been
Thou forever wilt be._

   – _"Great is Thy
     Faithfulness"_
   by Thomas
   Chisholm

_____

_____

_____

_____

_____

_____

_____

_____

_____

_____

_____

_____

_____

_____

_____

_____

_____

_____

_____

_____

_____

Day 5 ~

On pages 224-230, Chip listed four ways we can respond to the faithfulness of God. You probably thought of something that could fit in each category. Rather than just having good intentions, take some time to write down how you can make application in every area.

1. Is there something in my **past** I need to put behind me?

_____

_____

2. What **present** problems, pains, and failures can I bring to Jesus today?

_____

_____

3. How can I place my **hope** for the future in the One who will never let me down?

_____

_____

4. Who can I tell this **week** about how God has been faithful to me?

_____

_____

DIGGING DEEPER

Read chapter 15
in A. W. Tozer's *Knowledge of the Holy.*

"The Faithfulness of God"
Hebrews 10:23

INTRODUCTION — What's the Source of Your Hope?

Three Observations About the Human Species

We all depend on <u>something</u> or <u>someone</u> to "hold us up" inside.

When that <u>something</u> or <u>someone</u> is "coming through for us" we experience a sense of peace, satisfaction, and optimism about the future.

When that <u>something</u> or <u>someone</u> "fails to come through for us" we experience a sense of anxiety, dissatisfaction, and ultimately despair.

Conclusion: It seems that the secret to a life of unending joy and peace is to find <u>something</u> or <u>someone</u> **who will "come through for you" 100% of the time in any and every situation forever.**

The Solution= Lamentations 3:21–24

I.   <u>Defining "The Faithfulness of God"</u>

⁓ **Definition** – Steadfast in affection or allegiance (loyal), firm in adherence to promises or in observance of duty (conscientious), given with strong assurance (binding), true to the facts, to a standard (constant). – Websters

⁓ **Synonyms** – Dependable, trustworthy, loyal, staunch, resolute, constant, reliable, true to one's word, keeps one's promises, true to and consistent to one's character, someone "who comes through for you."

∼ **Why Is God Able to Be Faithful 100% of the Time?**

1. He is **<u>all-knowing</u>** – He is never caught off guard.
   Romans 11:33-36

2. He is **<u>all-power</u>** – He never encounters anything or anyone
   who can thwart His plans or purposes.

3. He is **<u>holy</u>** – He is pure, honest, full of integrity, unable to lie,
   and therefore, is always consistent with His character and His
   Word. Isaiah 6:1-6

4. He is **<u>eternal</u>** – He is not affected by space or time; He knows
   the end from the beginning. Psalm 90:2

5. He is **<u>omnipresent</u>** – Nothing can happen outside the sphere of
   His influence. Psalm 139:7-11

6. He is **<u>immutable</u>** – He never changes; is never different then
   He is now, He is never in a bad mood, and never has a bad day.
   Malachi 3:6, Hebrews 13:8

"All of God's acts are consistent with all of His attributes. No attribute contradicts any other, but all harmonize and blend into each other in the infinite abyss of the Godhead... God, being who He is, cannot cease to be what He is, and He is at once faithful and immutable, so all His words and acts must be and must remain faithful."

A.W. Tozer

Summary: God is 100% faithful to His Word, His promises, His people, and His character because He cannot be otherwise. **He will never let you down!**

II. God <u>Reveals</u> His Faithfulness to Us Through . . .

   ～ His _____ – Psalm 19:1-6; 57:10; 119:90; 145:13-6

   ～ His _____

       ～ The Patriarchs – Genesis 12:1-3
       ～ Israel – Micah 7:20
       ～ David – Psalm 132:11
       ～ The Church – Matthew 16:18

   ～ His _____ – John 14:15-18, Galatians 5:23

   ～ His _____ – Numbers 23:19, Isaiah 25:1

   ～ His _____ – Isaiah 55:10-11

       ～ His Word is true – John 17:17
       ～ He keeps His covenants – Deuteronomy 7:9
       ～ He keeps His promises – Hebrews 10:23
       ～ He fulfills His predictions – Isaiah 42:8-10

   ～ His _____ – Isaiah 11:5, Revelation 19:11

   ～ His _____ of our lives when . . .

       ～ We are <u>weak</u> – 2 Corinthians 12:9-10
       ～ We are <u>tempted</u> – 1 Corinthians 10:13
       ～ We <u>sin</u> – 1 John 1:9
       ～ We <u>utterly fail</u> – 2 Timothy 2:11-13

Small Group Questions

1. What one thing from the past do you need to release?

2. What current pain, problem, or failure do you need to bring Him today?

3. How can you help one another make this study the beginning of a life-changing process instead of a ten-week event?

NOTE: Next week is critical to our group's success. It's the Celebration Session. We will review, look back on our progress, fellowship, give thanks, and help you develop a game plan for long-term life transformation.

 From Head to Heart

> ### ~ Truth or Lie Card ~
>
> *Look at the appendix and you will discover your perforated "Truth or Lie" cards. There is one for each week. On the front you will write down a lie that you have believed contrary to God's **faithfulness**. On the back you will find a definition of God's faithfulness along with the memory verse for this past week. Review it every morning and night. Keep it close for the rest of your life.*

FACILITATOR T!PS

Someone may want to share in private and possibly with a Christian counselor and/or pastor. Allow them the freedom to approach you after the group.

Make sure you close each sensitive time with prayer.

Make sure people know they don't have to share if they don't feel comfortable.

God: As He Longs for You to See Him

IO

SESSION TEN

Time to Remember

"Papa, Papa," said the boy as he yanked on his grandfather's tunic, "what are these stones for?"

"Ah," leaning down, the grandfather pulled his grandson close, "let me tell you a story."

If the children of Israel forgot about the parting of the Red Sea, they would forget about God's power. If the children of Israel forgot about manna dropping from heaven, they would forget about God's provision. If the children of Israel forgot about the fire by night and the cloud by day, they would forget about His faithful presence.

So God asked them to set up some stones:

> *Now when all the nation had finished crossing the Jordan, the Lord spoke to Joshua, saying, "Take for yourselves twelve men from the people, one man from each tribe, and command them, saying, 'Take up for yourselves twelve stones from here out of the middle of the Jordan, from the place where the priests feet are standing firm, and carry them over with you and lay them down in the lodging place where you will lodge tonight.'" So Joshua called the twelve men whom he had appointed from the sons of Israel, one man from each tribe; and Joshua said to them, "Cross again to the ark of the Lord your God into the middle of the Jordan, and each of you take up a stone on his shoulder, according to the number of the tribes of the sons of Israel. Let this be a sign among you, so that when your children ask later, saying, 'What do these stones mean to you?' then you shall say to them, 'Because the waters of the Jordan were cut off before the ark of the covenant of the Lord; when it crossed the Jordan, the waters of the Jordan were cut off' so these stones shall become a memorial to the sons of Israel forever.'"*
>
> — Joshua 4:1-7

Over 40 times in the Bible, God tells his people to "remember." We are a people prone to short term memory loss. If we don't establish memorial stones in the landscape of our mind, we are apt to return to lies, misperceptions, and a fuzzy view of God.

This week, it's time to set up some stones. Ask yourself, "how has my view of God changed?" More importantly, "how has it changed me?" God longs for you to see Him clearly. Let's plan on remembering the view from here on.

Day I ～

Read the conclusion in *God: As He Longs for You to See Him*. How has your vision of God moved from cloudy to clear?

_____

_____

_____

_____

_____

_____

_____

_____

_____

_____

_____

_____

_____

_____

_____

_____

_____

_____

_____

_____

_____

_____

_____

Prayer for the Week:

O Lord, our Lord, there is none like Thee in heaven above or in the earth beneath. Thine is the greatness and the dignity and the majesty. All that is in heaven and the earth is Thine; Thine is the kingdom and the power and the glory forever, O God, and Thou art exalted as Head over all.

Amen.

But the lovingkindness of the Lord is from everlasting to everlasting on those who fear Him, and His righteousness to children's children, to those who keep His covenant and remember His precepts to do them. The Lord has established His throne in the heavens, and His sovereignty rules over all.

— Psalm 103: 17-19

Day 2 ～

Take some time to remember and reflect. As you look back over those first four attributes, what images or new insights do you have about each?

Goodness:

_____

_____

_____

_____

_____

Sovereignty:

_____

_____

_____

_____

Holiness:

_____

_____

_____

_____

Wisdom:

_____

_____

_____

_____

Day 3 ~

RENEW YOUR MIND

Our vision of who God is can be improved by a clear picture from His Word. Take a moment today to memorize and meditate on this verse:

> *For You are the Lord Most High over all the earth; You are exalted far above all gods.*
>
> — Psalm 97: 9

Are you reviewing your Truth or Lie Cards?

_____

_____

_____

_____

_____

_____

_____

_____

_____

_____

_____

_____

_____

_____

_____

_____

_____

_____

_____

Day 4 ~

Take some time to remember and reflect. As you look back over the last three attributes, what images or new insights do you have about each?

Justice:

_____

_____

_____

_____

_____

_____

Love:

_____

_____

_____

_____

_____

Faithfulness:

_____

_____

_____

_____

_____

_____

"I think it might be demonstrated that almost every heresy that has afflicted the church through the years has arisen from believing about God things that are not true, or from overemphasizing certain true things so as to obscure other things equally true."

— A. W. Tozer

Day 5 ~

Filled out journals will never guarantee life change. Knowledge never equals maturity; it's only gained through obedience. As we look back over these weeks, we've discovered how God longs to be seen. However, that picture will fade when the worries of this world command our attention, when the calendar fills back up, and when you come up against expected spiritual opposition in the next few weeks.

Knowing that, here is an **Emergency Game Plan** to help you take all this knowledge from your head to your heart:

1. *Find a two-hour block within the next 12-24 hours.* Maybe it's a long lunch. Maybe it's getting up extra early. Maybe it's going to a coffee shop rather than sitting in front of the television. But change rarely occurs without reflection, and reflection takes time. Once you have jotted down your thoughts, intentions, and applications, resist the temptation to formulate a bunch of new actions. Don't jump into a bunch of new activities, goals, and resolutions. You'll probably just set yourself up for failure. Remember, change requires reflection. Take 30 minutes a day for a week to pray, think, and ponder over the specific action points you feel like God is calling you to.

2. *Get the notes out of the journal.* These notes that you have taken will do little good up on your bookshelf. Whether you journal or not, it would be wise to record how God spoke to you through this study. Grab the top-level nuggets that you know you can apply to your life right now.

3. *Keep reviewing the cards.* Day by day, review the lies that you tell yourself and combat them with God's truth.

4. *Find a partner.* God never intended the Christian life to be played solo. It's a team sport. Find someone you can trust to share your game plan. Ask this person to commit to encourage, cheer, hold you accountable, and restore you as you dedicate yourself to this plan.

Read chapter 23
in A. W. Tozer's *Knowledge of the Holy.*

Time to Celebrate

God said to Moses, *"I Am who I Am;"* and He said, *"Thus you shall say to the sons of Israel, 'I Am has sent me to you.'"*

— Exodus 3:14

It is impossible to keep our moral practices sound and our inward attitudes right while our idea of God is erroneous or inadequate. If we would bring back spiritual power to our lives, we must begin to think of God more nearly as He is.

— A. W. Tozer

Give Thanks (Thoughts and Reflections):
John 3:12–14; John 14

_____

_____

_____

_____

_____

_____

_____

_____

_____

_____

_____

_____

_____

_____

_____

_____

_____

_____

Small Group Time

RETAKE THE VISION TEST

1. Those who know God have
   great energy for God.

Low Energy/
Vague Knowledge

High Energy/
Clear Knowledge

0   10

2. Those who know God have
   great thoughts of God.

Low Energy/
Vague Knowledge

High Energy/
Clear Knowledge

0   10

3. Those who know God show
   great boldness for God.

Low Energy/
Vague Knowledge

High Energy/
Clear Knowledge

0   10

4. Those who know God have
   great contentment in God.

Low Energy/
Vague Knowledge

High Energy/
Clear Knowledge

0   10

Now celebrate with each other!

 From Head to Heart

What was the application that God gave to your
small group? What is the passion on your heart as
a group? Focus on casting a vision for what God
will do next with your group. Maybe it's blessing a
couple or a person to lead others through this
material. Maybe it's deciding on another study.
Maybe it's taking a break and helping others on a
tangible level. But leave with a game plan.

FACILITATOR
T!PS

You may want to
ask your group
before you celebrate!
What was the
one big lesson
you received from
God because of
this study?

Also, find out one
habit from each
person that they are
starting as a result
of this study.

What's Next?

Small Group Studies offered by Chip Ingram.

GOD: AS HE LONGS FOR YOU TO SEE HIM

How would you describe God? Awesome? All Powerful? Creator? While we cannot know Him exhaustively, we can know Him truly. And God longs for you to see Him as He truly is. Join Chip in this fascinating series studying the seven attributes of God.

MIRACLE OF LIFE CHANGE

Is life change really possible? If we're honest most of us would answer, "No." You've tried numerous programs that promise big changes, but in reality, deliver very little results. You long for transformation, but don't know where to begin. There's good news for you and there is hope. Life change is possible!

r12: LIVING ON THE EDGE

Being a genuine disciple of Christ flows out of a relationship with Him. It's about experiencing God's grace, not earning His love through performance. A real relationship with Jesus Christ will produce a follower whose life looks progressively more like His life. Romans 12 provides a relational profile of an authentic disciple: someone who is surrendered to God, separate from the world's values, sober in self-assessment, serving in love and supernaturally responding to evil with good. Christians who live out this kind of lifestyle are what we call r12 Christians.

INVISIBLE WAR

Beneath our tangible landscape lurks an invisible spiritual realm where an unseen battle rages. It's real and it's dangerous. If you're prepared to remove the blinders and gaze into the unseen world, Chip is ready to take you there.

EFFECTIVE PARENTING IN A DEFECTIVE WORLD

Raising children is a tough challenge in today's world. Peers and pop culture exert a never-ending pressure on kids. Many come from split homes. But the good news is that God has been working with people from bad situations for a long time! In Effective Parenting you will learn how God's principles for raising children still work today. Packed with practical advice, this series will give struggling parents a vision for their children's future and life-changing help for today!

EXPERIENCING GOD'S DREAM FOR YOUR MARRIAGE

Would you like a fresh breeze to blow in your marriage? Do you long for a marriage where intimacy and communication are a reality instead of a dream? "Experiencing God's Dream for Your Marriage" is a topical series by Chip Ingram examining God's design for marriage, with practical instruction to help you make your marriage what God desires it to be.

FIVE LIES THAT RUIN RELATIONSHIPS

Have you ever looked back over a situation or relationship in your life and wondered how it became so messy or difficult? In Five Lies that Ruin Relationships, we'll define five of the most common lies that have the potential to ruin relationships with those we love. What we think about life determines how we live it, so there is power in knowing and applying God's truth when confronted with lies and discovering the freedom He longs for us to enjoy in our relationships.

LOVE, SEX & LASTING RELATIONSHIPS

Everyone wants to love and be loved. The pursuit of "true love" is everywhere you look! It's romanticized on TV and in the movies we watch. There are books about it, songs about it, internet dating, and even seminars on it... all of which are designed to "help" you find that special someone to love. So why is "true love" so elusive? Could it be that the picture of love we see in today's culture is nothing more than an illusion? If so, what does real love look like? In this series, you'll discover that there is a better way to find love, stay in love, and grow in intimacy for a lifetime. Chip Ingram delivers to us God's prescription for building relationships that last a lifetime.

TRUE SPIRITUALITY ACCORDING TO JESUS (r12)

True Spirituality According to Jesus is a small group study that complements the Living on the Edge book. The book looks specifically at Romans, chapter 12 and the small group study looks at what Jesus said and modeled for us about the principles in Romans 12. Taken together, this is a dynamic study that will encourage you to become an r12 Christian. Romans 12 is the START HERE for the Christian life. What most Christians sadly misunderstand is that God isn't into religious activities or performance-based Christianity. Instead, Romans 12 reveals to us a relational profile of what it means to be a disciple, as well as a proven pathway to becoming more like Jesus every day.

God: As He Longs for You to See Him

APPENDIX

Goodness of God

Lies I believe about
God's goodness…

_____
_____
_____
_____
_____
_____
_____
_____
_____

GOD: AS HE LONGS FOR YOU TO SEE HIM

God's Holiness

Lies I believe about
God's holiness…

_____
_____
_____
_____
_____
_____
_____
_____
_____

LIVING
ON THE EDGE

GOD: AS HE LONGS FOR YOU TO SEE HIM

Sovereignty of God

Lies I believe about
God's sovereignty…

_____
_____
_____
_____
_____
_____
_____
_____
_____

GOD: AS HE LONGS FOR YOU TO SEE HIM

God's Wisdom

Lies I believe about
God's wisdom…

_____
_____
_____
_____
_____
_____
_____
_____
_____

LIVING
ON THE EDGE

GOD: AS HE LONGS FOR YOU TO SEE HIM

Definition of God's Holiness:

We know nothing like the divine holiness.
It stands apart, unique, unapproachable, incomprehensible and unattainable. The natural man is
blind to it. He may fear God's power and admire
His wisdom, but His holiness he cannot even
imagine. Only the Spirit of the Holy One can
impart to the human spirit the knowledge
of the holy.

— A. W. Tozer

*As obedient children, do not be conformed to the former
lusts which were yours in your ignorance, but like the Holy
One who called you, be holy yourselves also in all your
behavior; because it is written, "You shall be holy, for I am
holy."*

— I Peter 1:14-16

Definition of God's Goodness:

The goodness of God is that which disposes Him
to be kind, cordial, benevolent,
and full of good will toward men. He is tender-hearted and of quick sympathy, and His unfailing attitude toward all moral beings is open,
frank, and friendly. By His nature He is inclined
to bestow blessedness and He takes total pleasure in the happiness of His people.

*"For the Lord God is a sun and shield; The Lord gives grace
and glory; no good thing does He
withhold from those who walk uprightly."*

— Psalm 84:11

Definition of God's Wisdom:

The wisdom of God tells us that God will bring
about the best possible results, by the best possible
means, for the most possible people, for the
longest possible time.

— Dr. Charles Ryrie

*Oh, the depth of the riches both of the wisdom and knowledge of God! How unsearchable are His
judgments and unfathomable His ways! For who
has known the mind of the Lord, or who became
His counselor? Or who has first given to Him that
it might be paid back to Him again? For from
Him and through Him and to Him are all things
to Him be the glory forever. Amen.*

— Romans 11:33-36

Definition of God's Sovereignty:

The sovereignty of God is that which
separates the God of the Bible from all
other religions, truth claims, or philosophies.

When we say God is sovereign, we declare that
by virtue of His creatorship over all life and reality, His all-knowing, all powerful, and benevolent
rule, that He is in fact the Lord
of all lords, King of kings, and in absolute control
of time and eternity. Nothing will come into my
life today that He did not either allow or decree
for my ultimate good.

*And we know that God causes all things to work together
for good to those who love God, to those
who are called according to His purpose.*

— Romans 8:28

*As for you, you meant evil against me, but God meant it
for good in order to bring about this present result, to pre-serve many people alive.*

— Genesis 50:20

Love of God

Lies I believe about God's love…

_____

_____

_____

_____

_____

_____

Faithfulness of God

Lies I believe about
God's faithfulness…

_____

_____

_____

_____

_____

_____

LIVING
ON THE EDGE

Justice of God

Lies I believe about
God's justice…

_____

_____

_____

_____

_____

_____

_____

_____

_____

_____

_____

_____

_____

_____

Definition of God's Faithfulness:

Upon God's faithfulness rests our whole hope of future blessedness... Only as we have complete assurance that He is faithful, may we live in peace and look forward with assurance to the life to come.

— A. W. Tozer

As so today, I choose to place my hope in you, Lord Jesus; because you have promised to "come through for me" 100 percent of the time in any and every situation forever.

This I recall to my mind, therefore I have hope. The Lord's lovingkindnesses indeed never cease, for His compassions never fail. They are new every morning; great is Your faithfulness. "The Lord is my portion," says my soul, "Therefore I have hope in Him."

— Lamentations 3:21-24

Definition of God's Love:

God's love is His holy disposition toward all that He has created that compels Him to express unconditional affection and selective correction to provide the highest quality of existence, both now and forever, for the object of his love.

For I am convinced that neither death, nor life, nor angels, nor principalities, nor things present, nor things to come, nor powers, nor height, nor depth, nor any other created thing, will be able to separate us from the love of God, which is in Christ Jesus our Lord.

— Romans 8:38-39

Definition of God's Justice:

God is just. That means all He is and all He does is accomplished with perfect integrity, fairness, righteousness, and impartiality. Justice is not a standard God follows; He is the standard. Though full of goodness, infinite in love, and merciful to the repentant, God's justice demands moral equity and eternal retribution for deeds done in the body. God's justice means no one will receive a "raw deal" in the final analysis. I can trust that He will one day balance the scales.

Never pay back evil for evil to anyone. Respect what is right in the sight of all men. If possible, so far as it depends on you, be at peace with all men. Never take your own revenge, beloved, but leave room for the wrath of God, for it is written, "Vengeance is mine, I will repay," says the Lord. "But if your enemy is hungry, feed him, and if he is thirsty, give him a drink; for in so doing you will heap burning coals on his head." Do not be overcome by evil, but overcome evil with good.

— Romans 12:17-21